BOOK OF JOY

EXPANSE

First published in Great Britain 2016 by Century
This edition published in Great Britain 2023 by Expanse
An imprint of HarperCollins*Publishers*
1 London Bridge Street, London SE1 9GF
www.farshore.co.uk

HarperCollins*Publishers*
Macken House, 39/40 Mayor Street Upper,
Dublin 1 D01 C9W8, Ireland

ISBN 978 0 00 861421 8
Printed in Bosnia and Herzegovina
001

This book is produced from independently certified FSC™ paper
to ensure responsible forest management.

For more information visit: www.harpercollins.co.uk/green

"Yes, Pokémon evolve, and their Trainers grow older – but while everything changes, one thing remains true always. Friends can be friends forever, and even if they seem a little different, sometimes you have to look with your heart and not your eyes."

- NARRATOR -

"Anytime I've been sad or happy or really mad about something, **Pokémon have always been there by my side, through it all.**"

- *ASH* -

Dear Reader,

Like our heroes Ash and Pikachu, we are all on a road to personal mastery. Whether we want to become the greatest Trainer in the world, to develop into a more powerful being, or just to become the best version of ourselves, we are all at different points along life's winding path.

But like the seasoned Pokémon Trainer who has thrown too many Poké Balls to count, our journey in life is never easy.

For every battle won, a battle elsewhere is lost. For every Jigglypuff evolved, an Igglybuff is forever changed. For every inspirational Brock we meet, a Team Rocket member is lurking in the bushes, ready to pounce.

During the tough times in life, we must be calm and good-spirited. Like Ash, we must believe in ourselves and play to our strengths. Our journey may be long, and we must exercise patience. If we move too quickly, we can go backwards, not forwards. Only if we rely on the kindness of others, and if we cherish our friends, will we make our lives our most wonderful adventures.

This book's wisdom has been amassed over the course of many adventures across the Pokémon world. Within its chapters you will discover simple but powerful philosophies that can change every aspect of your life. From tender expressions of love and friendship, to inspiring calls to follow your dreams; from hard fought lessons about failure, to sage advice on victory and happiness.

*Whether through the actions of Team Rocket, the moral
fortitude of our heroes, or anything in between, one thing
is clear: any situation faced is an opportunity to learn!*

*Cherish this book's wisdom and act out its philosophy as
much as you can in your daily life. Remember: a heart can
be so true that our courage will pull us through!*

CHAPTER ONE

BELIEF AND COURAGE

———

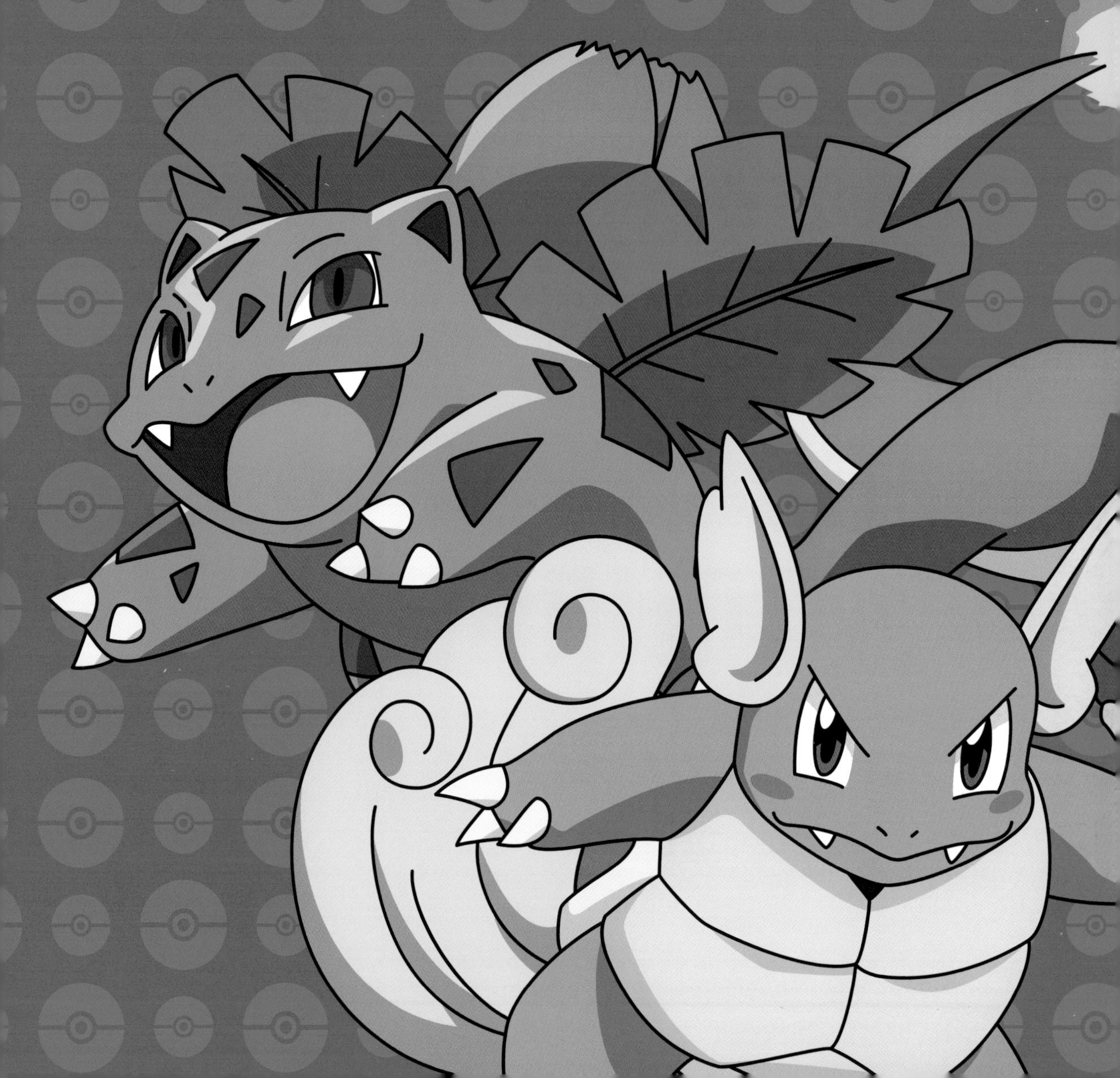

"I will travel across the land
Searching far and wide
Each Pokémon to understand
The power that's inside."

– Pokémon Theme –

"The first thing you need to do is calm your mind. If you observe closely with a calm mind, you'll be able to discern the important things."

- *RAMOS* -

"Adventure Rule Number Four: You never give up until the very end! Cause there's always gotta be a way out. You get it?"

- ASH -

"When you got lemons, you make lemonade; and when you got rice, you make rice balls."

- BROCK -

"It's just like Wela volcano, burning within my heart should always be *THE DESIRE TO BE STRONG.*"

- KIAWE -

"*Cryin' don't help.*
I already tried that."
- *MEOWTH* -

"I wanna be the very best like no one ever was."

– Pokémon Theme –

"You have to
find the
*FUN IN
EVERYTHING!*"

- CHLOE -

"Do Your *BEST!*"

- PROFESSOR OAK -

"And when you see a *shooting star* you *make a wish*."

- *MALLOW* -

"I've gotta keep going! Keep … going… going … gone … I've gotta work out more often."

- *MEOWTH* -

"I trust that if I don't give up,

MY DREAMS WILL COME TRUE!"

- SOPHOCLES -

"All I could do was watch, and it made me wish that I could grow up quick so I could do that too."

- MAX -

"A heart so true our courage will pull us through."

– Pokémon Theme –

"WHINING
only makes you
HUNGRIER"

- MEOWTH -

"**Just be confident.** You can do anything you set your mind to."

- DELIA KETCHUM -

"Take on every challenge … and *rise above them all!*"

- *GRACE* -

"We're all on the road to make our dreams come true. *FULL SPEED AHEAD!*" -

ASH -

"Just keep on doing your best."

- *MISTY* -

"Focus on the here and now. It's the first day of the rest your life."

- MEOWTH -

"Every challenge along the way
With courage I will face
I will battle every day
To claim my rightful place."

– Pokémon Theme –

"Remember, I'm the top cat.

MEOWTH!"

- MEOWTH -

CHAPTER TWO

BATTLES

—

"We may be mean and nasty, but we'd never turn our backs on a ***teammate in trouble***."

- JESSIE, TEAM ROCKET -

"Hey, chill out kid, cool your flame! Now, who would want to have fisticuffs on a nice moonlit night like this?"

- *MEOWTH* -

"If you get all caught up with the things that are right in front of you, *you may lose sight of what's important.*"

- RAMOS -

"Feeling frustrated?
*Then use all that frustration
and get out of there!*
Do it!"

- ASH -

"This Pokémon's got guts! My guts are busting … "

- *MEOWTH* -

"Everybody, stay *calm!*"

- *SERENA* -

"Use more than one
Pokémon if you're
afraid to lose"

- GIOVANNI -

"For everyone who cheered
us on, all the way here ...
and for the Pokémon, too!
I'VE GOTTA WIN THIS!"

- ASH -

"When fortune smiles on you, you must smile on back."

- JESSIE, TEAM ROCKET -

CHAPTER THREE

WORK

—

"Everything takes time, Magikarp – **it took me three years to grow this moustache.**"

- QUINCY -

"There's no harm if we slow it down just a little bit!"

- ASH -

"The progress of science stops the moment you give up. If you don't give up, *ANYTHING IS POSSIBLE!*"

- CLEMONT -

"We may not make a lot of money, but we *sure have got our freedom.*"

- *JESSIE* -

"*There are some things you just can't learn at school*, and that's a good lesson."

- GISELLE -

"A strategy – so they've been planning a new way *to lose*."

- *L.T. SURGE* -

"I can guarantee you one thing for sure: No matter what else happens, I'm going to keep on working *toward my dream.*"

- DAWN -

"If we all dance together, *it'll be more fun!*"

- SERENA -

"MINIMAL EFFORT WITH MAXIMUM PROFIT!

That's the Team Rocket way!"

- TEAM ROCKET -

"You should mind your Ps and Qs and Pikachus."

- *MEOWTH* -

CHAPTER FOUR

LOVE

——

"You bet. It doesn't matter if you're catching Pokémon or battling: Making sure you ***do it all with your heart is the most important thing of all.***"

- ASH -

"Looks like friendship's **stronger** than jealousy."

- *BROCK* -

"There's nothing wrong with wanting to hold onto precious things from the past. But becoming overly attached can **keep you stuck in the past.**"

- *WOODWARD* -

"You can't judge a Pokémon by its *SMELL*."

- *NARRATOR* -

"It's a lot easier to like someone who likes you than to like someone who doesn't."

- MISTY -

"We believe in
love power.
That's because
WE LOVE POWER."

- CASSIDY AND BUTCH -

"There's no sense in going out of your way just to get someone to like you."

- ASH -

"You always know what everybody needs and that's a part of you I love."

- LANA -

"It's okay if *we're not perfect.*"

- *SERENA* -

"How **romantic** can you get?"

- *IRIS* -

"A little Pokémon
love power works
miracles!"

- *CASSIDY* -

"Pikachu, I CHOOSE YOU!"

- ASH -

"It seems the world
I'm looking for and the
world you're looking for
are not the same …

But we can still get along!"

- N -

CHAPTER FIVE

Friendship

—

"I wanna make friends with all the Pokémon in the world."

- *ASH* -

"This calls for a poem!"

- *PROFESSOR OAK* -

"Character is another word for *TROUBLEMAKER ...*"

- MAY -

"It's better to make up quickly after a fight, rather than drag it out."

- *CILAN* -

"I'll be with you in spirit, even when we're apart."

- GOH -

"Best of friends till the end!"

- GARY -

"Our
NEW CHALLENGE
is just beginning,
right, Pikachu?!"

- ASH -

"You helped me out so much! After meeting you, I was finally able to become friends with Pokémon."

- LILLIE -

**"Come with me,
the time is right,
There's no better team,
Arm in arm we'll win the fight,
It's always been our dream."**

– Pokémon Theme –

"Recognise what's in each other's hearts. That's what counts."

- OFFICER JENNY -

"But if you want people to be kind to you, *you should be kind to them first.*"

- CHLOE -

"Well if we all just treated our Pokémon and each other with the kind of **care** and **love** and **respect** we'd deserve, the world would be picture perfect."

- TRACEY -

155

"I think we were meant to meet and *become friends*."

- *ASH* -

"We are only going to have smiles from here on in. This is the place where the fun never ends."

- WATTSON -

"The longer you wait, the harder it'll be for either of you to apologise!"

- *CILAN* -

"We can say our goodbyes and still laugh together."

- BONNIE -

"You've got buddies
who'd give you the
shirts off their backs
if you needed them."

- MEOWTH -

"There's nothing we could ever do that's a waste of time!"

- ASH -

CHAPTER SIX

MASTERY

—

"Pikachu!"

- *PIKACHU* -

"We haven't lost anything yet! There's no reason to give up!"

- *ASH* -

"Being nervous is only natural. I was always that way before a race. And that's when you need to tell yourself: *It's time to go for broke!*"

- *GRACE* -

"*FAILURE LEADS TO SUCCESS!* That's how truly great inventions get perfected."

- *LILIA* -

"No matter how crazy you have to be, *never stop striving for victory.*"

– *GOH* –

"Don't think of it as failing, think of it as not succeeding!"

- *MEOWTH* -

"If I really think about it, I'd rather do stuff! *'Cause even if I goof up, I learn something.*"

- ASH -

"One can only
advance so far
**relying on strength
and intuition.**"

- PROFESSOR OAK -

185

"Don't try to chase after it. *Relax, and let it come to you.*"

– *ASH* –

"Thinking too much won't help. For now, I've got to keep *moving forward!*"

- SERENA -

"Sometimes certain things you'd never think would go together, end up going together really well!"

- DAWN -

BIBLIOGRAPHY

All quotes in this book are sourced from the Pokémon animated series,
licensed by The Pokémon Company International, Inc.

3. Showdown At Linoone, 5. Ash And N: A Clash Of Ideals!, 15. Pokémon Theme, 16. The Green, Green Grass Types Of Home, 18. Team Plasma And The Awakening Ceremony, 20. Pokémon Paparazzi, 22. A Crowning Moment Of Truth!, 24. A Shroomish Skirmish, 27. Pokémon Theme, 28. Nightfall? Nightmares!, 30. An Old Family Blend!, 32. Showering The World With Love!, 34. So You're Having A Bad Day!, 36. Lighting The Way Home!, 38. Home Is Where The Start Is!, 41. Pokémon Theme, 42. Pokémon Shipwreck!, 44. Pokémon Showdown!, 46. A Race For Home!, 48. Dreaming A Performer's Dream!, 50. Gotta Catch Ya Later!, 52. Tears For Fears!, 55. Pokémon Theme, 56. Showdown In Pewter City, 58. Pokémon Showdown, 62. Go West, Young Meowth!, 64. Tears For Fears!, 66. The Green, Green Grass Types Of Home, 68. A Rush Of Ninja Wisdom!, 70. So You're Having A Bad Day!, 72. Master Class Choices!, 74. The Battle Of The Badge, 76. Battling As Hard As Stone!, 78. So You're Having A Bad Day!, 82. The Wacky Watcher, 84. A Ruin With A View, 86. A Watershed Moment!, 88. Holy Matrimony, 90. The School Of Hard Knocks, 92. Electric Shock Showdown, 94. Four Roads Diverged In A Pokémon Port!, 96. A Frolicking Find In The Flowers! , 98. Mantine Overboard, 100. The Wacky Watcher, 104. Battling The Bully!, 106. Chikorita's Big Upset, 108. Mending A Broken Spirit!, 110. Pokémon Scent - Sation, 112. The Heartbreak Of Brock, 114. The Training Center Secret, 116. Once In A Mawile, 118. Battling Besties!, 120. Master Class Choices!, 122. Cottonee In Love!, 124. The Training Center Secret!, 126. The Water Flowers Of Cerulean City, 128. The Name's N!, 132. The Rainbow And The Pokémon Master, 134. The Ties That Bind, 136. A Corphish Out Of Water, 138. The Path That Leads To Goodbye!, 140. Not Too Close For Comfort!, 142. Ill - Will Hunting!, 144. Kalos, Where Dreams And Adventures Begin!, 146. Thank You, Alola! The Journey Continues!, 149. Pokémon Theme, 150. The Case Of The K - 9 Caper, 152. Everybody's Doing The Underground Shuffle!, 154. The Joy Of Pokémon, 156. Gotta Catch Ya Later!, 158. Watt's With Wattson, 160. The Path That Leads To Goodbye! 162. Dreaming A Performer's Dream!, 164. Clamperl Of Wisdom, 166. Performing A Pathway To The Future!, 170. Pokémon I Choose You!, 172. The Cave Of Mirrors!, 174. Master Class Is In Session!, 176. A Keeper For Keeps?, 178. Making Battles In The Sand!, 180. The Ultimate Test!, 182. Performing A Pathway To The Future!, 184. Friends To The End, 186. Wired For Battle, 188. Master Class Choices!, 190. Double - Time Battle Training!